Chip was in a toy shop.

He put his backpack by the ducks.

A boy put his backpack by the ducks.

"Look at this rocket," said Chip.

"My cash is in my backpack," he said.

Mum got a backpack.

But it was not Chip's backpack.

The boy had Chip's backpack.

Chip had the boy's backpack.

Chip was upset.

That boy has my cash.

"Let's get it back," said Mum.

Mum and Chip ran …

… to this shop …

… to that shop.

The boy and his mum got on a bus.

"Stop that bus," said Mum.

The bus did stop.

Chip got his backpack back.